Illustrations by Romain Simon
Text by David Eden

CHIN·CHIN,
the panda

BRIMAX BOOKS   CAMBRIDGE   ENGLAND

Common Koklas

Not long ago a mother Giant Panda sat hugging her baby in her arms. The baby's name was Chin-Chin.
Chin-Chin was only a few months old, but already he was quite heavy. He and his mother lived in the thick bamboo forest high in the mountains of South West China. They sat on a nest made from pieces of bamboo.

6

Chin-Chin and his mother loved to eat bamboo. She had big strong heavy teeth to chew even the hardest sticks. Chin-Chin's teeth were not so strong. He ate only the soft tender shoots. When he was a year old he lost his baby teeth and grew strong new teeth for chewing hard bamboo.

Reeve's Pheasant

Red or Lesser Panda

One day, Chin-Chin went walking with his mother. They saw a beautiful animal with black legs and a long bushy tail. "Look," said Chin-Chin's mother. "That is your cousin, the Red Panda."

10

The Red Panda spent most of his time in the treetops.
Every morning and evening he came down to the ground to
feed on young bamboo shoots, or anything he could find,
such as roots or acorns or leaves. As soon as he saw the
Giant Pandas, the Red Panda leapt nimbly onto some rocks.

"Please stop to play." said Chin-Chin.
"We won't hurt you," said his mother.
"Not today," replied the Red Panda.
"I must go back into the trees for a
little nap."

11

After the Red Panda had run off, Chin-Chin went back to
his nest to play by himself. He rolled about on his back.
If you look carefully at his feet you can see his five
claws. Like all Giant Pandas he had a special extra thumb
on his front feet which he used to hold bamboo sticks.
Because he was able to hold the bamboo canes in his paws,
Chin-Chin could sit up straight to eat like a human being.
No other animal except the Red Panda has a special thumb.
Some Giant Pandas can feed themselves with a spoon.

12

"I think I will have a bite to eat now," thought Chin-Chin. He broke off a tender young bamboo cane and ate it. He scratched his back against his favourite pine tree and sat down to rest.

One day, when he was a little older, Chin-Chin left his
mother's side and went looking for food by himself.
He climbed up the mountainside, through the bamboo forest,
and past the rhododendron forest which grows above it.
At last he came to a valley where the winter's snow
had not melted. Suddenly he saw a beautiful snow leopard
who had come to the valley to look for food.
14

The snow leopard is a
very rare creature.
It lives by hunting for
wild sheep, musk deer,
and other small animals.
It has a long tail,
thick fur, and large
pads to give it a good
grip on ice and snow.

Snow Leopard

15

Chin-Chin was not afraid
of the snow leopard. He
went back through the
rhododendron forest.
"Hallo panda," said a
cheerful little jay.
"Hallo," said Chin-Chin.
He plodded on his way
down the steep hillside.

Black Throated Jay

16

17

When he next left the bamboo forest, Chin-Chin found some
tasty finger-shaped mushrooms which he enjoyed very much.
Although they live mainly on bamboo shoots, pandas can
eat many different kinds of food if they find them,
including meat. They move from one favourite feeding
place to another all through the year.

18

As soon as he had finished,
Chin-Chin climbed a tree.

Cabot's Tragopan

Young pandas often climb
into a tree. They hug the
trunk with their strong
arms and legs. Older
pandas are less nimble.

White Crested Laughing Thrush

19

Red Capped Babbler

Black Crowned Babbler

Soon after he had come down from the tree, Chin-Chin discovered some crocus bulbs. He scratched them out of the ground with his paws and ate them up, flowers as well.

20

Bearded Vulture

High up in the sky
three Bearded Vultures
were looking for food.
They would eat any dead
animal they could find.

Chin-Chin went slowly on his
way. He certainly did not
expect his next adventure!

21

While walking in a valley below a village, Chin-Chin met a man named Ma. Ma picked him up and put him in his knapsack. "Come with me, my fine panda. I shall take you to the zoo."

Ma locked Chin-Chin in a bamboo pen and went into his house to tell his family about the panda. Chin-Chin was very sad. 'I wish I could fly like that bee,' he thought.

Chin-Chin was determined to get out of prison. Early in the morning he beat at the pen with his strong paws. Before long he had made a hole just big enough to squeeze through.

Chin-Chin did not try to hurry away from Ma's house.
Pandas always walk slowly wherever they want to go,
because their bodies are heavy and awkward. Besides,
they are not afraid of anyone or anything.
Just as he was about to leave the village, Chin-Chin
came upon a beehive. Now Chin-Chin liked honey very much.
'I think I will stop for a bite of honey,' he thought.

24

Chin-Chin upset the hive with
his paw. Soon he was licking
the honey. His thick fur
protected him from the bees.

As soon as he had finished with the hive, Chin-Chin went back into the forest. He climbed into a tall pine tree, where he felt safe.
"No one will steal me from here," he said to himself.

Chin-Chin quickly forgot all about Ma. He climbed down backwards from the tree and went to find food. Soon he came to a stream "I know," he thought, "I will go fishing."

26

Chin-Chin stood on a
wet rock. Suddenly his
foot slipped. SPLASH! He
fell into the water.
"Ha ha ha!" said the
sure-footed Musk Deer.

Musk Deer

27

Chin-Chin decided to go fishing another day after all.
He walked through the forest until he came to some eggs
laid by a pair of pheasants who had made their nest on
the ground. In spite of all the birds could do to stop
him, Chin-Chin ate up the eggs. They were delicious.

Reeve's Pheasants

29

Soon after he had eaten
the eggs Chin-Chin found,
a more shallow stream.
There were many streams in the mountains. Some of them
had very powerful currents. They could carry large boulders
along. Chin-Chin waded up to his knees in the water.
He waited patiently for some time until he saw a fish.
He chased it with his paw, but it was gone in a flash.
30

Once again Chin-Chin stood very still. After a few moments he saw a lovely trout. SWISH! He scooped it from the water with his paw. It landed on a rock, where he soon ate it.

Full of fresh
fish, Chin-Chin
sharpened his
claws on a tree.
Forest life went
on as usual.

Brown Eared Pheasant

32

Goral

The Goral is an animal which
is like both the goat and
the antelope.

It lives in the steep river gorges. In summer it eats
grass and small plants. In autumn it moves to the forest
for leaves and nuts. In winter it lives on bare branches.

33

Suddenly a herd of wild pigs trotted by. Chin-Chin often used to see them, because they travelled along the same forest trails as the Giant Pandas.

Wild pigs eat bulbs, nuts, grubs, insects and anything they can root out with their snouts. They are sometimes very fierce, but they do not attack the Giant Panda. The black and white markings of the panda warn enemies to keep away. Pandas can bite savagely when they wish.

One autumn morning, just as he was finishing his
breakfast of bamboo shoots, Chin-Chin heard a
flock of wild geese go honking overhead.
He looked up. The geese were flying very high on
their way to a warmer country for the winter.
Few birds fly higher than wild geese.

"Hallo panda," said the Serow. But Chin-Chin was too busy eating bamboo shoots to reply.

Serow

Himalayan Monal Pheasant

38

Takin

Himalayan Black Bear

The Serow and the Takin are both goat-antelopes like the
Goral. They live on the plants of the steep mountainsides
and gorges. The Takin is larger than the Serow and Goral.
The Takin ran away when he saw the black bear, who might
kill him if he caught him.
The black bear lives mostly on nuts, berries, and grubs.
Unlike brown bears, it does not hibernate in winter.

The first snow of winter began to fall, but Chin-Chin took
no notice. He plodded slowly on his way through the
forest. When the snow lies really thickly on the bamboos

the pandas make a tunnel through them which is used by the
other animals as well.
"Why should I care about winter?" asked Chin-Chin.
"I am a Giant Panda. We pandas are lords of the forest."
40

FOR THOSE WHO WOULD
LIKE TO KNOW MORE

Brown Bear

Raccoon

For many years no one could decide what sort of animal a panda is. Although it looks very like a bear, it is in some ways related to the raccoon. The teeth of a panda are not like those of a bear, nor can a panda walk about on its hind legs like a bear. On the other hand, a new-born panda is very small, like a new-born bear. In fact, the Giant Panda is really close only to the Red Panda. Giant Pandas live wild in the Chinese province of Szechwan. One day Chinese zoologists may be able to tell us more about them.

Map of China, showing the province of Szechwan, home of the Giant Panda.

When they are in the zoo, some pandas are very playful. They will play with an old lorry tyre or a big plastic ring. If they have a ball it has to be especially strong or they burst it with their claws. Sometimes they will bathe in a bath tub, or perhaps drink the water! In hot weather zoo pandas like to lie on a block of ice or stand under a cold shower. They have air-conditioned cages to keep them cool in summer and warm in winter.

Pandas, after a Chinese watercolour

The Chinese names for the Giant Panda are "bei-shung", which means "white bear", and "shung-mao", which means "bear-cat", or as we would say, "cat-bear". In Europe the panda has been called "Bamboo Bear" or "Harlequin Bear". The scientific name for the Giant Panda means "The panda-footed animal which is black and white". Pandas are very rare animals. To make sure they do not become extinct the Chinese Government has banned all hunting of them and established nature reserves for them. Most of the zoo pandas live in Chinese zoos. Not long ago China sent two pandas to London Zoo. Chinese zoos have also managed to breed pandas in captivity.

SHUNG -- BEAR

DA -- GREAT

MAO -- CAT

Emblem of the World Wildlife Fund

SOME FACTS AND FIGURES ABOUT PANDAS

HISTORY

The Red Panda was discovered in 1821. The Giant Panda was discovered
by the French priest Father Armand David in 1869. The first living
Giant Panda to leave China was a baby named Su-Lin, who came to an
American zoo in 1936. Three Giant Pandas came to London Zoo in
1938. Chi-Chi came to London Zoo in 1958. Chia-Chia and Ching-Ching
came to London Zoo in 1974. Ming-Ming was born in Peking Zoo in 1963.

WEIGHT

A new-born panda is about as big as a small kitten. It weighs only
about 100 grammes. It grows rapidly until when it is weaned at the
age of six months it weighs 10 or 12 kilos. A fully grown adult
male panda may weigh about 140 kilos. A fully grown adult female
may weigh about 110 kilos.

LIFESPAN

A panda in a zoo lives for about 15 years. Wild pandas are said to
live for 25-30 years.

DIET

In the zoo pandas will eat many things, including spaghetti and jam!
Usually they are given a mixture of rice, maize, bone meal, soya
bean, eggs, salt, and sugar. This mixture is given twice a day.
For the rest of the time they eat bamboo shoots, which are grown
specially for them. A zoo panda who is not given bamboo may grow
fat, or perhaps even come to dislike bamboo.